Tuffy and Boots

GATES – HUBER – SALISBURY

Tuffy
and Boots

ARTHUR I. GATES
MIRIAM BLANTON HUBER
FRANK SEELY SALISBURY

THE MACMILLAN COMPANY : NEW YORK

Stories

Illustrated by
CHARLES PAYZANT AND ASSOCIATES
HELEN HANSEN, SYLVIA HOLLAND, JANET PAGE,
BASIL DAVIDOVICH, ERNEST TERRAZAS

Tuffy

3

Mother! Mother!
Look at Tuffy.
Look at Tuffy play.

4

Father! Father!
Look at Tuffy.
Look at Tuffy run.

Ted! Ted!
Look at Tuffy.
Look at Tuffy jump.
Look at Tuffy run and jump.

6

Tuffy! Tuffy!
Look at Boots.
Look at Boots splash.

Splash! Splash! Splash!

7

Come, Tuffy.
Come to Sally.
Come, Tuffy, come.

Tuffy and Boots

Tuffy likes Ted.
Tuffy likes Sally.
Tuffy likes Boots.

10

Tuffy likes to play.

Tuffy likes to play with Boots.

Tuffy likes to run and play.

Tuffy likes to play.

He likes to play with Ted.

He likes to play with Sally.

He likes to play with Boots.

Tuffy likes to jump and play.

12

Sally said, "Look, Mother.
Look at Tuffy."

Ted said, "Look at Tuffy.
He likes Mother."

Mother said, "Look.

Boots likes to play.

He likes to play with Tuffy."

Sally said, "Run, Tuffy.
Run, Tuffy, run!"

Ted said, "Run, Boots.
Run, Boots, run!"

Ted and Sally

Father said, "Go and play.
Go and play, Ted.
Go and play, Sally."

Ted and Sally like to play.

Father said, "Go up, Sally.
Go up, up, up."

Ted said, "Look at Sally.
Look at Sally go up."

Father said, "Go up, Ted.
Go up, up, up."

Sally said, "Look at Ted.
Look at Ted go up."

20

Father said, "Go down, Ted.
Go down."

Sally said, "Go down, Ted.
Go down, down, down.
Father, look at Ted.
Look at Ted go down."

Ted and Sally go up.
Ted and Sally go down.

Up and down!
Up and down!
Ted and Sally go up and down.

Ted and Tuffy

Sally said, "Here, Tuffy.
Come here, Tuffy.
Come and play.
Come and play with Sally."

Ted said, "Look, Sally.
Look up.
Look up, Sally.
Here is Tuffy.
Here he is."

Sally said, "Come down, Tuffy.
Come down. Come down!"

Ted said, "Come down, Tuffy.
Come down here and play."

Sally said, "Ted! Ted!
Get Tuffy.
Go up and get Tuffy.
Go up and get Tuffy, Ted."

Ted said, "Here I go.
Here I go, Sally.
Here I go to get Tuffy."

28

Sally said, "Mother! Mother!
Come here and look at Ted.
Ted will get Tuffy.
Tuffy likes Ted.
He will come down with Ted."

Mother said, "Tuffy! Tuffy!
Come down, Tuffy.
Come down with Ted."

Sally said, "Look, Mother.
Tuffy will come down with Ted."

Ted said, "Here I come, Sally.
Here I come with Tuffy.
Here he is."

Sally said, "Tuffy! Tuffy!"

Mother said, "Come, Ted.
Come with Mother.
Sally will play with Tuffy."

Ride with Father

Father said, "Come, Ted.
Come, Sally.
Come and ride."

Ted said, "Here we come.
Here we come, Father.
We like to ride."

Ted said, "Here is Boots.
He wants to ride."

Sally said, "Father!
I want Tuffy to ride.
We will go and get Tuffy."

35

Sally said, "Tuffy! Tuffy!
We want you, Tuffy.
Come and ride, Tuffy."

Ted said, "Come, Tuffy.
Come and ride.
We want you, Tuffy."

36

Mother said, "Jump in, Tuffy.
Jump in and ride.
Jump in, Tuffy, jump in.
We want you to ride."

37

Mother said, "Come, Ted.
Come, Sally."

Ted said, "Mother.
We want Tuffy to ride."

Father said, "Get in, Ted.
Get in, Sally."

Sally said, "Father.
I want Tuffy to ride."

Father said, "He will ride.
Tuffy will ride, Sally."

Ted said, "Look, Sally.
Here is Tuffy."

Sally said, "Tuffy! Tuffy!
Father! Mother!
Tuffy is here."

The Boats

41

Sally said, "Look, Ted.
See the boats!
See the boats!"

Father said, "Come, Mother.
We will go in here.
We will go and see the boats."

Ted said, "See the big boat.
See the big boat, Sally.
I want the big boat."

Sally said, "Look, Ted.
See the little boat.
I want the little boat."

Sally said, "Look, Ted.
Here is the boat you want."

Ted said, "Look, Father.
Here is the boat I want.
Will you get the big boat?
Here it is."

Father said, "I see it, Ted.
We will get the big boat."

Sally said, "Look, Mother.
Here is the little boat.
Here is the boat I want.
I like it, Mother.
Will you get the little boat?"

Mother said, "I like it, Sally.
I like the little boat.
We will get it, Sally."

45

Ted said, "Look, Mother.
See the big boat.
See the little boat.
Here we go with the boats."

Sally said, "Big boat!
Little boat!
We will play with the boats."

The Big Boat

Ted said, "Here, Boots.
See my big boat.
We will play with it."

Sally said, "Here, Tuffy.
See my little boat.
We will play with it."

Ted said, "Look, Sally, look.
See Boots run.
See Tuffy run.
Look at Boots and Tuffy run."

Sally said, "Ted! Ted!
Here comes Boots.
Look, Ted, look.
Oh! Oh! Oh!"

Down go Ted and the boat.
Down, down.

Ted said, "Oh, Sally.
Look at my boat.
Look at my big boat."

"Oh! Oh! Oh!" said Sally.

Sally said, "Here, Ted.
Here is the little boat.
Play with my boat.
I want you to play with it.
Here it is, Ted."

Ted said, "Oh, Sally!
I want my big boat."

Ted said, "Oh, Father!
Look at my boat.
Look at my big boat."

Father said, "Come, Ted.
I will look at it."

Sally said, "Come, Ted.
We will go with Father."

Ted said, "Oh, Father!
Will it go?
Will my big boat go?"

Father said, "We will see.
We will see, Ted."

Ted said, "Oh! Oh! Oh!
I want my boat to go."

Sally said, "Look, Ted.
See Father.
See the boat.
The boat will go, Ted."

Ted said, "Father! Father!
Will my big boat go?
Will it go, Father?"

Father said, "It will go.
Come, Ted.
Come, Sally.
We will see the boat go."

Splash and Ride

Sally said, "Look! Look!
Look at the boat.
Splash, big boat, splash!"

Ted said, "Oh, Father!
See the big boat.
See the big boat go."

Ted said, "Look, Boots.
My big boat will go.
Look at it, Boots.
Go, big boat, go!"

Sally said, "Look, Tuffy.
Here is my little boat.
Come and see it.
Come and see it go.
Go, little boat, go."

Mother said, "See the boats.
See the boats go."

Sally said, "Oh, Mother!
Look at my little boat.
Ride, little boat, ride."

Ted said, "Look at Boots.
See Boots splash."

Sally said, "See the boats.
See the boats go up and down.
Up and down."

Father said, "Here, Boots.
Come here, Boots."

Ted said, "Go, big boat, go.
Ride, big boat, ride."

Sally said, "Go, little boat.
Go! Go! Go!
Ride, little boat.
Ride! Ride! Ride!"

To be read to children

Five Kittens

Five kittens are as warm as sun.
So close they are, they look like one.

You look for noses; there are three.
Four little tails are all you see.

You hear a puppy bark and scare.
Five kittens run then everywhere!

But when the dog goes — warm as sun,
So close they are, they look like one.

Grateful acknowledgment is made to Joseph Joel Keith for the use of the poem, "Five Kittens," written for this book; all rights reserved.

Word List

The following list contains all the new words—26 in number —that occur in *Tuffy and Boots*, second basal pre-primer of *The Macmillan Readers*. The 14 words introduced in *Splash*, first pre-primer, are repeated, making a total pre-primer vocabulary of 40 words.

All of the new words, except the proper name, *Tuffy*, are words frequently found in children's reading.

1.	14.	27. get	40.	52.
2.	15.	28. I	41. the	53.
3. Tuffy	16.	29. will	boats	54.
4.	17.	30.	42. see	55.
5.	18. go	31.	43. big	56.
6.	19. up	32.	little	57.
7.	20.	33. ride	44. it	58.
8.	21. down	34. we	45.	59.
9.	22.	35. wants	46.	60.
10. likes	23.	36. you	47.	61.
11. with	24. here	37. in	48. my	62.
12. he	25. is	38.	49	63.
13. said	26.	39.	50. oh	64.
			51.	

The Macmillan Readers